Little Pearl's CIRCUS WORLD

Based on the true story of Pearl Clark LaComa

GW00656670

Written By Charmain Zimmerman Brackett

Based on the journals of Juanita LaComa Zimmerman

Illustrated by Erica Pastecki

Layout design by Ashlee Henry

Copyright 2014 by Charmain Zimmerman Brackett. All rights reserved.
ISBN-10:0985625953   ISBN-13:978-0-9856259-5-5

I love it when the circus comes to town. It's so exciting. When the circus arrives, there's a big parade. Music from the calliope wagon calls everyone outside to watch the clowns, acrobats, and animals make their way down the dusty main street. People clap and cheer. They wave at me, and I wave back to them.

My name is Pearl; the newspapers call me "Little Pearl."
I've been performing in my Papa's circus since I was four.

People are excited to see the circus. There's not a lot of entertainment especially in small towns in the early 20th century. People come to the big top to see the show. Sometimes, they bring picnics with them so they can spend the whole day with us.

People call my dad "M.L." That's short for Mack Loren. I call him "Papa." His circus is named after him. It's the M.L. Clark and Son's Combined Shows.

Papa loves horses. Before he started the circus, he owned a ranch in Texas. Horses are very important to the circus. I have a white horse I ride on in the parade, and I also ride him into the ring when I get ready to perform.

I'm what they call a contortionist. I have a hard time saying that word, but that's what they put in the newspaper about me. I don't remember when I started doing tricks. I'm really flexible. I can bend over backward, and I can stand on my head. I can keep my balance on a ball, too.
Because I can do all of that, the newspapers called me "the boneless wonder."

Since I'm in the main tent with my act, I get to wear all kinds of pretty costumes. I get to wear feathers in my hair too. I like those. My Mama buys ballet slippers for me to wear. They have pretty ribbons that tie around my ankles.

Papa and Mama say I'm a natural-born performer. I love being in front of the people, hearing them clap makes me smile. I know I did something to make them happy.

I can sing and dance too. I think I get that from Mama. She sang and danced on stage with her family before she met Papa.

We have all kinds of wild animals in our circus. People call that a menagerie. We have black-maned lions, elephants, jaguars, pumas, dogs, a camel, a llama, and lots and lots of horses traveling with the show.

There are about 200 horses with the show. Some are performers, and some are work horses. We need them to help pull the circus wagons that carry the animals and the props we need for the show.

The circus wagons are our homes when we travel. There aren't a lot of places like hotels for us to stay. We go to many small towns. We sleep in the wagons at night. When I get bigger, I'll have a wagon car of my own.

I'm not the only performer in the circus. We have clowns and musicians, but some of the animals perform too. I love the animals especially the elephants. One of the elephants is named Mena. People love her; she's the biggest elephant in a circus. She's 11 feet tall and weighs 12,000 pounds.

Even though she's big, I think Mena could be a dancer. She can stand on a tub and balance on two of her legs; then she balances on her other legs. She makes me laugh. She's funny to watch.

Mena and the other elephants are fun to watch when they aren't performing too. The circus travels a lot. When we are in places with rivers and lakes, the elephants love to play in the water. They take the water in through their trunks and spray it in the air. They make a sound like a trumpet. I'd love to be in there with them. Sometimes, they don't want to leave.

Mena likes the other elephants, but her best friend is Mose the Camel. They go everywhere together.

The elephants are helpful too. Traveling on dirt roads can be hard especially when it rains. The wheels of the wagons get stuck in the thick mud, and the elephants help push the wagons.

When we get to town, sometimes, a field will have to be cleared of tree stumps. The elephants are so strong. They can pull them out of the ground with no problems at all. They also help raise the poles of the big tent.

Not only are elephants smart and helpful, they are curious. One time, the elephants decided they wanted to take a walk and explore the new place we visited.

I guess they were hungry that morning. They found a little house near a farm. Breakfast must have smelled good. One of the elephants reached his trunk in the open window and helped himself to their food.

I wish I could have seen the faces of the family. They must have been really surprised.

Papa had to pay them for their breakfast and for some of the corn the elephants trampled. He gave them tickets, and they came to see the show.

I'm so happy to be a part of the circus with my family. I don't ever want to leave it. When I get older, I'm going to fly through the air on a trapeze, and I'll be able to see all of the people looking up at me.

My circus world is an exciting place.

GLOSSARY

Acrobat - a performer who does gymnastics

Calliope - a musical instrument that looks like an organ, but its sound is made by steam whistles. The name comes from Calliope who was the Greek goddess of music.

Contortionist - an acrobat who can twist his or her body into difficult and sometimes unnatural positions.

Menagerie - a collection of wild animals

Puma - another name for a cougar

Trapeze - a swing used by acrobats in the circus

The Real
CIRCUS GIRL

WAIT **ONLY GREAT SHOW** COMING

M. L. CLARK & SON'S SHOWS

WILD ANIMALS
WILD WEST EXHIBITION

One Ring, One Act, One Feature at a Time
SO YOU CAN SEE AND HEAR EVERYTHING UNDER OUR HUGE
HAPPY DAYS SUN AND RAIN PROOF TENTS

MENA The Largest Elephant
IN CAPTIVITY
WEIGHT 12,000 POUNDS

MOSE
The Biggest
CAMEL ON EARTH

BARNIE
THE LARGEST and MOST
FEROCIOUS BLACK MANED
African Lion

GRAND FREE STREET PARADE
THE GREATEST
FREE EXHIBITION TWICE DAILY AT 1 AND 7 P. M.

PEARL CLARK LACOMA

The story of Little Pearl is based on the real life of Pearl Clark LaComa who was born into a family of circus owners on Christmas Eve 1890. At the time, Pearl's father, Mack Loren "M.L." Clark was partnered with his brother, Wiley, and the two owned the Clark Bros. Circus. By 1894, M.L. was on his own, and his circus became known as the M.L. Clark and Son's Combined Shows.

From all accounts, Pearl was a natural performer. Her father was a charismatic showman who ran the dog and pony act in the circus' early days. Pearl's mother, Amelia Frances "Fannie" Frazier Clark, was also a performer and tended to an elephant named Empress. She had been part of a vaudeville show prior to getting married. Pearl was a featured performer when she was only 4 years-old. Known as a contortionist, she was dubbed "the boneless wonder" by the age of 14 for her flexibility.

The M.L. Clark and Son's Combined Shows' home base was in Alexandria, La., where M.L. owned a large amount of property. The circus opened in Alexandria at the beginning of many seasons before it headed to small towns across the United States taking its menagerie of animals with them. Some years, the circus would travel as many as 3,400 miles across dirt roads with only horses to draw the circus wagons. At one time in its history, there were as many as 200 horses with the show. There were a variety of other animals in the circus including several elephants. Mena was the largest elephant in captivity weighing 12,000 pounds and standing 11 feet tall. Despite her massive size, she had a mild-mannered temperament and was playful and extremely loyal. She was described as almost being a pet, and she could have been the elephant who helped herself to a farm family's breakfast, as described in the book. One of her companions was a two-humped camel named Mose. Other animals include a black-maned lion named Barnie. There were llamas, pumas and hyenas in the circus.

Not only did the elephants perform, but they helped in a variety of ways such as clearing lots when the circus came to town and pushing out wagons stuck along muddy roads.

A few weeks before the circus arrived in town an advance man riding a horse-drawn wagon would announce it was coming. When the performers arrived in town, there was a grand parade. In 1906, the entire M.L. Clark menagerie was featured in the Mobile, Ala. Mardi Gras parade, and it was announced in the entertainment newspaper, The New York Clipper,

that it would do so annually.

Besides the performing animals, there were clowns, jugglers, and musicians in the circus.

Pearl had a big personality in a tiny frame. As an adult, she was only 4'8". She would make a dramatic entrance into the ring on a white horse. She continued working as a contortionist, but she did finally take to the sky on the trapeze with her husband. William Christopher "Cris" LaComa joined the circus when he was a teenager. He was part of group of aerialists known as the LaComa Troupe. He and a few of his brothers had been working in a tire factory in Akron, Ohio, around 1906. One day, they decided to quit their jobs and join the circus. They changed their last names and never looked back. Pearl and Cris were married around 1909.

Pearl and Cris' firstborn daughter, Juanita LaComa Zimmerman, arrived on Dec. 23, 1912. She might have been born in a circus wagon except that Pearl insisted she be taken back to Alexandria, La. to give birth. They were in California at the time, and it was a long journey. But even having a baby couldn't keep Pearl from performing. When it was time for their act, they'd leave the baby in a hammock made by tying a sheet between two tent posts, where according to Juanita's own writings she "slept peacefully."

The couple had two more children, Hazel and William Christopher. They got out of the performing side and had a vaudeville act and a traveling movie house for a few years. But it wasn't long before they were back in the ring.

They included the children in the act. Hazel and Juanita sang and danced. Circus performers or "show people" didn't have a good reputation though, and this was hard on Juanita. She didn't like people staring at her and talking about her; so she retired from the circus as a teen.

Pearl called the circus the "red wagons," and she told her daughter she'd follow the red wagons until the day she died. She did just that. Her father, M.L., died on Oct. 4, 1926, and his obituary was placed on the front of the Alexandria newspaper, The Town Talk. The obituary stated Pearl was in San Antonio at the time and was too ill to travel home for the funeral. She died on Feb. 1, 1927 at the age of 36 from tuberculosis.

A few years after M.L.'s death, his son, Lee, sold the circus, and it closed for the final time in 1945.

M. L.
CLARK & SONS
COMBINED
SHOWS

M.L. CLARK

LEE CLARK

TO - NIGHT

PEARL CLARK

And
Her
ompany
of
efined

VAUDE.
VILLE
ENT

LACOMAS
Moving Picture Show—
COMBINED.
High Class Show for Ladies, Gentle-
men and Children. Under a
WATERPROOF TENT.
DOORS OPENED AT 7:30 SHARP.

PRICES

PEARL CLARK
THE PRIMA DONNA
WITH THE
LA COMAS VAUDEVILLE
SHOW

This book is dedicated to my grandmother, Juanita LaComa Zimmerman, Dec. 23, 1912 - Oct. 22, 1998, whose dream was to become a writer. I hope that by taking the anecdotes she wrote in spiral-bound notebooks that I have helped to fulfill that dream in a small way.

From the author

I'm the great-granddaughter of Pearl Clark LaComa and the granddaughter of Juanita LaComa Zimmerman. I was inspired to write about Little Pearl after meeting with my cousin, Becky Zimmerman Bagshaw, in May 2012.

I had grown up in Georgia after the Army sent my dad, Leonard Zimmerman Sr. to Fort Gordon. His family lived in Las Vegas and Houston, Texas. I didn't know much about my circus heritage until Becky began sending me photocopies of our grandmother's writings and family photographs. My grandmother had wanted to become a writer, but that dream was not fulfilled in her lifetime. After Juanita's death in 1998, circus memorabilia and photographs were divided among family members.

As a longtime journalist with a love of history, I knew I needed to gather this amazing bit of my family history into one place. I traveled to Baraboo, WI, Alexandria, LA, Seattle, WA, and Houston, TX to gather photographs and tidbits of information plus I spent countless hours scouring the internet for any searches of "M.L. Clark and Son's Combined Shows" and various other searches.

I posted family photos online, and others encouraged me to pursue writing a book about my family's circus past. Without enough information for a full-length book, I decided to try a children's book instead.

This book brings together family history and photographs in one place and fulfills my grandmother's desire to become an author because much of the book is based on her simple stories in spiral-bound notebooks.

Special thanks to Stefanie Reed, the angel of this project.
Also many thanks to Kat Trabert and the Greater Augusta Arts Council for your support in this project.
Also thank you - Lisa Talley, Becky Zimmerman Bagshaw and Michele Zimmerman for holding onto pieces of the family history so this book could be completed.
Acknowledgements - Peter Shrake with the Robert L. Parkinson Library and Research Center in Baraboo, Wisconsin; Ernie West, Galveston Memorial Park, Galveston, Texas; Phil Tate, DeLeon Texas History.

8956694R00018

Printed in Great Britain
by Amazon.co.uk, Ltd.,
Marston Gate.